JOHN C. MAXWELL

LEARNING
THE 21 IRREFUTABLE
LAWS OF
LEADERSHIP

Study Guide

Dear Friend,

You and your team are about to embark on an exciting journey. As I look back over my 30-year career, I recognize that nothing has been more exciting than process of learning how to become a better leader.

As you prepare to train and equip your leaders using *Learning the 21 Laws of Leadership*, you are making an incredible investment — in your people, your organization, and your future. It really is true: Everything rises and falls on leadership. And as you prepare your people to become better leaders, you will begin to receive the benefits of the Law of the Inner Circle, which says, "A Leader's Potential is Determined by Those Closest to Him."

Before you get your people started, I want to encourage you to watch the introductory video and read *The 21 Irrefutable Laws of Leadership*. Spend some time wrestling with the principles and assimilating them. My recommendation is that you read a law each morning for 21 days, taking time throughout that day to reflect on it and its implications to your organization. Once you have a firm handle on the principles contained in the book, you will have a good foundation for facilitating the group learning time for your people.

Then begin training your leaders. Ask them to read the book first as well. Then introduce them to the videos. You will make the greatest impact on them if you teach them one law per week. Show the video and then facilitate a discussion, not only helping them understand the law, but emphasizing how to apply it to their lives.

It won't be long before you begin seeing results. Each time your people get another law under their belt, they will become better leaders. And if they can get all 21, the impact on your organization will be unbelievable.

The INJOY Group and I appreciate you and your desire to become a better leader. Keep growing and keep leading.

Your friend,

John C. Maxwell

John C. Maxwell

P.S. Don't forget to keep investing in your own leadership development. Get *Living the 21 Laws of Leadership* and use it over the next 21 months to take your leadership to the highest level.

The 21 Irrefutable Laws of Leadership
Dr. John C. Maxwell

Follow Them and People Will Follow You

When the country is in chaos, everybody has a plan to fix it —
but it takes a leader of real understanding to straighten things out."
—Prov. 28:2" (The Message)

The Qualifying Tests to Become Leadership Laws

1. Not based on _____, _____ or _____.

2. Relate and apply to _____ communities.

3. Recognized by other _____ as Leadership Laws.

4. Stand the test of _____.

Observations:

1. These laws can be _____.

2. These laws stand _____.

3. These laws carry _____.

   If only Robert McNamara had known the Law of Solid Ground.
   The War in Vietnam — and everything that happened at home because of it —
   might have turned out differently.

4. These laws are the _____ of leadership.

   The Intentional Process of Raising Leaders:

   The Book: *The 21 Irrefutable Laws of Leadership* = A Picture of the Laws

   _____

   Audio Tapes. *Living the 21 Laws of leadership* = A Personal Application of the Laws

   _____

   Video Tapes: *Learning the 21 Laws of Leadership* = A Corporate Application
   of the Laws

   _____

1.The Law of the _____

Leadership Determines the Level of Effectiveness

"When good people run things, everyone is glad, but when the ruler is bad, everyone groans."
—Prov. 29:2 (The Message)

Questions:

(1) What is the Lid # on my leadership? _____

(2) Would those around me agree with my assessment?_____

(3) What is my plan to increase my Lid # ? _____

(4) What are the Lid #'s of those that work with me? _____

                        Names   (#1–10)

_____   _____

_____   _____

_____   _____

_____   _____

_____   _____

(5) What is my plan to increase their Lid #'s ? _____

Evaluate Your Mastery of the Law of the Lid (1–10) _____

Resources:	Five Levels of Leadership	Video Kit	$119.95	T1109
	Leadership Limitations	MIC Tape	$12.00	I5026
	Lifting People to a Higher Level	ILC Tape	$12.00	C5122
	Developing the Leader Within You	Book	$17.95	B2014

To order these resources or for more information please call 1-800-333-6506

2. The Law of _____

The True Measure of Leadership is Influence — Nothing More, Nothing Less

It's not the *Position* that makes the *Leader* —
It's the *Leader* who makes the *Position!*

The best way to test a leader is to ask them to lead a _____ organization.

The 5 Levels of Leadership (Influence)

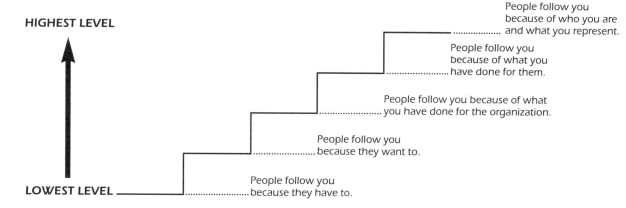

HIGHEST LEVEL

People follow you because of who you are and what you represent.

People follow you because of what you have done for them.

People follow you because of what you have done for the organization.

People follow you because they want to.

LOWEST LEVEL

People follow you because they have to.

Questions:

(1) What is the level of my influence with the leaders of my organization? _____

(2) What is the level of my influence with the followers of my organization? _____

(3) Who are the top 10 influencers of my organization? _____

(4) Do I influence the influencers? _____

Evaluate your mastery of the Law of Influence (1–10) _____

Resources:				
Taking an Influence Inventory	MIC Tape	$12.00	I5029
The 5 Levels of Leadership	Video Kit	$119.95	I5029
Becoming a Person of Influence	Book	$19.99	B2139
Be a People Person	Book	$6.99	B2002A

3. The Law of _____

Leadership Develops Daily, Not in a Day

"Like the horizons for breadth and the ocean for depth, the understanding of a good leader is broad and deep."

—Prov. 25:3 (The Message)

We _____ the event and _____ the process!

The Event	**The Process**
Encourages _____	Encourages _____
_____People	_____ People
Is a _____Issue	Is a _____Issue
_____ People	_____ People
Is _____	Is _____

Leadership is Many Faceted:

(1) _____   (5) _____

(2) _____   (6) _____

(3) _____   (7) _____

4) _____   (8) _____

The secret of our success is found in our _____ agenda.

What Can be Discovered in our Daily Agenda?

(1) _____   (4)_____   (7) _____

(2) _____   (5)_____   (8) _____

(3) _____   (6) _____   (9) _____

Champions don't become champions in the ring — they are merely recognized there!
—Unknown

Questions:

(1) Do I have a daily plan to grow as a leader? _____

(2) Do I have a leadership growth plan for my team? _____

(3) Am I developing a leadership culture in my organization? _____

(4) What are the evidences of a leadership culture? _____

Evaluate Your Mastery of the Law of Process (1–10) _____

Resources:			
INJOY Life Club	Monthly Tape Clubs	$36.00 quarterly by credit card C5QCC
Maximum Impact	Monthly Tape Clubs	$36.00 quarterly by credit card I5QCC
Serving Today	Monthly Tape Clubs	$33.00 quarterly by credit card L5QCC
100 Lessons on Leadership	Tape Kit	$250.00 C5007
The 21 Irrefutable Laws of Leadership	Book / Video Tapes	$17.99 B2143
Living the 21 Laws of Leadership	Audio Tapes	$189.95 B2143T
The Success Journey	Book	$19.99 B2133

To order these resources or for more information please call 1-800-333-6506

4. The Law of _____

Anyone Can Steer the Ship, but It Takes a Leader to Chart the Course

"A good leader remains focused. Controlling your destination is better than being controlled by it."

—Jack Welch

"A leader is one who sees _____ than others see.

A leader is one who sees _____ than others see.

A leader is one who sees _____ others see."

—Leroy Eims

"Realistic leaders are objective enough to minimize illusions.
They understand that self-deception can cost them their vision."

—Bill Easum

P _____   A _____

L _____   H _____

A _____   E _____

N _____   A _____

                                  D _____

The Secret of the Law of Navigation: _____

It's not the size of the project that determines its acceptance, support, and success. It's the size of the leader.

Questions:

(1) Do I know where I am going? _____

(2) Should I take my people with me? _____

(3) If so, what is the process? _____

(4) Have I shared the vision and the process with my leaders? _____

(5) Have I received their input and blessing? _____

_____

Evaluate Your Mastery of the Law of Navigation (1–10) _____

Resources:	Communicating to Change Lives	Video / Audio Kit	$139.95	T1154
	Casting a Courageous Vision	Video / Audio	$20.00	V3017
	Preparation—The Separating Between Winning and Losing	ILC Tape	$12.00	C5132

God, the Great Navigator / Leader
"Good leadership is a channel of water controlled by God; He directs it to whatever end He chooses."

—Prov. 21:1 (The Message)

5. The Law of _____

When the Real Leader Speaks, People Listen

Positional leaders have a title but not always a _____.

Real leaders have a following but not always a _____.

Positional leaders influence _____ people.

Real leaders influence _____.

Real Leaders become Real Leaders because of _____ — Who they are

Real Leaders become Real Leaders because of _____ — Who they know

Real Leaders become Real Leaders because of _____ — What they know

Real Leaders become Real Leaders because of _____ — What they feel

Real Leaders become Real Leaders because of _____ — Where they've been

Real Leaders become Real Leaders because of _____ — What they've done

Real Leaders become Real Leaders because of _____ — What they can do

---

Questions:

(1) Am I a real leader? _____

(2) Who are the real leaders in my organization? _____

(3) Do I have an excellent relationship with the real leaders? _____

(4) If not, why not? _____

Evaluate Your Mastery of the Law of EF Hutton (1–10) _____

"A good leader motivates, doesn't mislead, doesn't exploit." —Prov. 4:10(The Message)

Resources:			
Ten Commandments of a Communicator	ILCTape	$12.00	C5052
Power of Passion	ILC Tape	$12.00	C5095
Communicating to Change Lives	Video / Audio Kit	$139.95	T1154

6. The Law of _____

Trust is the Foundation of Leadership

Trust is the glue that holds an organization and its leader together.

To build trust, you must demonstrate CONSISTENT _____ +

CONSISTENT _____ .

A leader cannot continue to break trust with people and continue to influence them.

"Good leaders abhor wrongdoing of all kinds; sound leadership has a moral foundation."
—Prov. 16:12 (The Message)

Questions:

(1) Do I have "change in my pocket?" _____

(2) Is my "change" increasing or decreasing? _____

(3) Do I pass the integrity test? _____

_____

_____

Evaluate your mastery of the Law of Solid Ground. (1–10) _____

The Integrity Test

With integrity — The longer I lead, the _____ it gets.

Without integrity — The longer I lead, the _____ it becomes.

Resources:				
Paul, A Leader Who Lasted	ILC Tape	$12.00	C513A
Faith in the Man at the Top	ILC Tape	$12.00	C5034
Becoming a Man of God's Word	PK Video	$14.95	V2001
Five Levels of Leadership	Video Kit	$119.95	V3009

7. The Law of _____

People Naturally Follow Leaders Stronger Than Themselves

People don't follow people by accident.

When people respect you as a person, they _____ you.

When people respect you as a friend, they _____ you.

When people respect you as a leader, they _____ you.

**The more leadership ability a person has, the more quickly
he recognizes leadership — or it's lack — in others.**

How a Leader Gains Respect
"Leadership gains authority and respect when the voiceless poor are treated fairly."
                              —Prov. 12:14 (The Message)

(1) _____

(2) _____

(3) _____

(4) _____

(5) _____

(6) _____

The Test of Respect

(1) The response of the people when the leader asks for _____

(2) The response of the people when the leader asks for _____

Questions:

(1) Do I possess the qualities that earn respect? _____

(2) Do those closest to me respect me? _____

Evaluate your mastery of the Law of Respect. (1–10) _____

Resource: "R–E–S–P–E–C–T, Tell Me What You Think of Me" ILC Tape $12.00   C5114

8. The Law of _____

Leaders Evaluate Everything With a Leadership Bias

"Who you are determines what you see."

Leaders are _____ . . . They Read and Respond

They Read and Sense . . .

(1) _____   (5) _____

(2) _____   (6) _____

(3) _____   (7) _____

(4) _____   (8) _____

"A leader of good judgement gives stability; an exploiting leader leaves a trail of waste."
—Prov. 29:4(The Message)

Questions:

(1) Do I continue to get "blindsided" by people and events around me? _____

(2) Do others think ahead better than me? _____

(3) If so, who are they? _____

(4) Do I rely on others to help me with their intuitiveness? _____

Evaluate Your Mastery of the Law of Intuition. (1–10) _____

Resources:				
	How Leaders Think	ILC Tape	$12.00	C5102
	Insights Into Intuition	ILC Tape	$12.00	C507A
	Thinking Your Way to the Top	ILC Tape	$12.00	C5139

9. The Law of _____

Who You Are Is Who You Attract

Write down the top 3 qualities in people that you would like to attract to your organization.

(1) _____

(2) _____

(3) _____

Al McGuire: _"A team should be the extension of the coach's personality. My teams were arrogant and obnoxious."_

Key Areas of Attraction:

(1) _____   (4) _____

(2) _____   (5) _____

(3) _____   (6) _____

Questions:

(1) Does our mission statement reflect who we are or who we want to be? _____

(2) Are there changes I need to make to attract qualities that I do not possess?

_____

_____

Evaluate your mastery of the Law of Attraction. (1–10) _____

Resources:

What to Look For in a Leader	ILC Tape	$12.00	C5125
Relationships, They Make or Break Me	ILC Tape	$12.00	C5027
Attitudes that Give you Altitude	ILC Tape	$12.00	C5044
Developing Leaders to Make a Difference	Audio Kit	$139.95	T1133

10. The Law of _____

Leaders Touch a Heart Before They Ask for a Hand

The ability to "connect" with people is essential to strong leadership.

> **You can't move people to action unless you first move them with emotion. The heart comes before the head.**

All great communicators have one thing in common . . . they _____ with people.

Connecting with people is the _____ responsibility.

How to Connect with People

(1) Connect with _____.

(2) Share with _____ and _____.

(3) Live your _____.

(4) Know your _____.

(5) Communicate on _____ level.

(6) Give _____ totally to the people and the message.

(7) _____totally in the people and the message.

(8) Share how the message has touched _____.

(9) Offer _____ and _____.

> **On Boss's Day in 1994, a full—page ad appeared in _USA Today_. It was contracted and paid for by the employees of Southwest Airlines, and it was addressed to Herb Kelleher, the company's CEO.**

THANKS, HERB

For remembering every one of our names.
  For supporting the Ronald McDonald House.
For helping load baggage on Thanksgiving.
  For giving everyone a kiss (and we mean everyone).
For listening.
  For running the only profitable major airline.
For singing at our holiday party.
  For singing only once a year.
For letting us wear shorts and sneakers to work.
  For golfing at The LUV Classic with only one club.
For outtalking Sam Donaldson.
  For riding your Harley Davidson into Southwest Headquarters.
For being a friend, not just a boss.

Happy Boss's Day From Each One of Your 16,000 Employees.

Questions:

How well do I connect with others in the following areas?

A. Speaking _____

B. Conversation _____

C. Small Group Meetings _____

D. Board Meetings _____

Evaluate your mastery of the Law of Connection. (1–10) _____

"Good-tempered leaders invigorate lives; they're like spring rain and sunshine."
                              —Prov.16:15(The Message)

Resources:			
"What Every Leader Should Know About People"	ILC Tape	$12.00	C5138
Be a People Person	Book	$6.99	B2002A
Becoming a Person of Influence	Book	$19.99	B2139
Developing Leaders After God's Own Heart	Audio Kit	$139.95	T1144

11.The Law of _____

A Leader's Potential is Determined by Those Closest to Him

"The best executive is the one who has sense enough to pick good men to do what he wants done, and self restraint enough to keep from meddling while they do it."
                                                                                —Teddy Roosevelt

Inner Circle Commitments

(1) _____

(2) _____

Evaluation Tool

_____Value — Those who raise up themselves.

_____Value — Those who raise up the morale of the organization.

_____ Value — Those who raise up the leader.

_____Value — Those who raise up others.

_____ Value — Those who raise up people who raise up people.

(3) _____

"Good leaders cultivate honest speech; they love advisors who tell them the truth."
                                                                —Prov. 16:13 (The Message)

Questions:

(1) What is the average leadership # of my key laity? _____

(2) Do I have a leadership development program for them? _____

(3) What is the average leadership # of my staff? _____

(4) Do I have a leadership development program for them? _____

Evaluate Your Mastery of the Law of the Inner Circle. (1–10) _____

Resources:	Staffing With Excellence	Audio Kit	$129.95	DR008
	The Soul of INJOY	ILC Tape	$12.00	C5135
	Searching for Eagles	ILC Tape	$12.00	C5107
	How to Select a Supporting Cast	ILC Tape	$12.00	C5113

To order these resources or for more information please call 1-800-333-6506

12. The Law of _____

Only Secure Leaders Give Power to Others

The people's capacity to achieve is determined by their leader's willingness and ability to empower.

Why Do Leaders Fail to Empower Others?

(1) _____

(2) _____

(3) _____

(4) _____

It's amazing what can be accomplished if the leader doesn't care who gets the credit.

(5) _____

You can't lead people if you need people.

Questions:

(1) What is my Empowerment # ? _____

(2) If it is low, revisit the section "Why Do Leaders Fail to Empower Others?" _____

In which areas are you weak? _____

Evaluate Your Mastery of the Law of Empowerment. (1–10) _____

Resources:			
Security or Sabotage	ILC Tape	$12.00	CS141
Lifting People to a Higher Level	ILC Tape	$12.00	C5122
How to Get Out of Your Own Way	ILC Tape	$12.00	C5058
The Portrait of a Leader	MIC Tape	$12.00	I502A
Developing the Leader Within You	Book	$17.95	B2014

13. The Law of _____

It Takes a Leader to Raise Up a Leader

We teach what we know — We reproduce what we are!

It takes a Leader to _____ a Leader.

It takes a Leader to _____ a Leader.

It takes a Leader to _____ a Leader.

Q. "Why don't all leaders develop other leaders?

(1) They are _____.

(2) They spend too much time with _____.

(3) Followers are easier to find and lead than _____.

(4) They don't recognize the _____ of developing leaders.

(5) Leadership has been viewed as a _____ effort,

not a _____ one.

Questions:

(1) Am I reproducing leaders in my life?_____

(2) If not, why not? _____

Reproduction Strategy:

(1) Make a _____ commitment to reproduce leaders.

(2) Create an _____ that attracts potential leaders.

(3) Develop a system to _____ and _____ potential leaders.

(4) Provide Leadership training _____.

Evaluate Your Mastery of the Law of Reproduction. (1–10) _____

Resources:
Personal Growth Training — ILC and MIC Monthly Tapes $36.00 per quarter

Basic Leadership Training Strategy:
Book — *The 21 Irrefutable Laws of Leadership* — For all leaders $17.99   B2143
Audio — Living the 21 Irrefutable Laws of Leadership
— Teaching Application $189.95   B2143T

Other Leadership Resources: Board —
Developing Leaders to Make a Difference — 1st Year $139.95   T1133
Developing Leaders After God's Own Heart — 2nd Year $139.95   T1144

Potential Leaders:
Joshua's Men $119.95   DR001
Mentoring Women $119.95

Retreats:
Developing the Leader Within You   Video $199.00   B2014K
Developing the Leaders Around You   Video $199.00   B2057K

Books:
The 21 Laws of Leadership — 1st Book for all Leaders $17.99   B2143
Developing the Leader Within You — 2nd Book for all Leaders $17.95   B2014
Shoulder to Shoulder — Inner Circle People $10.99   DR007
The Winning Attitude — Leadership Position People $11.00   B2007
Becoming a Person of Influence — Leadership Position People $19.99   B2139
The Success Journey — Young Potential Leaders $19.99   B2133
Developing the Leaders Around You — Advanced Leaders — Staff $19.95   B2057

To order these resources or for more information please call 1-800-333-6506

14. The Law of _____

People Buy Into the Leader, Then the Vision

Every message is filtered through the _____

"The mark of a good leader is loyal followers;
Leadership is nothing without a loyal following." —Prov. 14:28(The Message)

When the Followers don't like the Leader or the Vision,
they look for another _____.

When the Followers don't like the Leader but they like the Vision,
they look for another _____.

When the Followers like the Leader but not the Vision,
they change the _____.

When the Followers like the Leader and the Vision,
they accomplish the _____.

The Leader finds the_____ and then the _____ .

The People find the _____ and then the _____ .

Questions:

(1)Have the people bought into me?(1–10) _____

(2)Have I bought into the people? (1–10) _____

Evaluate your mastery of the Law of Buy—In. (1–10) _____

"It's wonderful when the people believe in the leader.
It's MORE wonderful when the leader believes in the people."

Resources:				
Vision . . . The Process of Passing it On	Audio Kit	$40.00	T1109
The Value of Vision	ILC Tape	$12.00	C504A
What Followers Expect from Leaders	ILC Tape	$12.00	C5074

15. The Law of _____

Leaders Find a Way for the Team to Succeed

> **Victorious leaders find the alternative to winning unacceptable, so they find out what needs to be done to achieve victory, and then they go after it with everything at their disposal.**

Lincoln never forgot that the nation's victory was his highest priority, ahead of his own pride, reputation, and personal comfort. He surrounded himself with the best leaders possible, empowered his generals, and was never afraid to give others the credit for the Victories the Union gained. For example, following General Grant's victory at Vicksburg, Lincoln sent a letter to him saying, "I never had any faith, except the general hope that you knew better than I . . . I now wish to make the personal acknowledgment that you were right and I was wrong."

Jefferson Davis, on the other hand, never made victory his priority. When he should have been thinking like a revolutionary, he worked like a bureaucrat. When he should have been delegating authority and decision—making to his generals — the best in the land — he spent his time micro—managing them. And worst of all, he was more concerned with being right than with winning. Historian David M. Potter says of Davis, "He used an excessive share of his energy in contentious and even litigious argument to prove he was right. He seemed to feel that if he were right that was enough; that it was more important to vindicate his own rectitude than to get results." Davis violated the Law of Victory, and as a consequence his people suffered terrible defeat.

> **What is our aim? I answer in one word:**
> **Victory — victory at all costs,**
> **victory in spite of all terror, victory,**
> **however long and hard the road may be;**
> **for without victory there is no survival.**
>
> —Winston Churchill

What does the Law of Victory look like?

_____ is Responsible

_____ is Unacceptable

_____ is Unquenchable

_____ is Essential

_____ is Unthinkable

_____ is Unquestionable

_____ is Inevitable

"When good people are promoted, everything is great, but when the bad are in charge, watch out!"

—Prov. 28

Questions:

(1) Does my team consistently win?_____

(2) If not, why not? Start by reviewing, what the Law of Victory looks like. _____

_____

Evaluate Your Mastery of the Law of Victory. (1—10) _____

Resources:				
	Characteristics of a Giant Killer	ILC Tape	$12.00	C5119
	Why Winners Win	ILC Tape	$12.00	C5093
	Marching Off the Map	ILC Tape	$12.00	C509B
	How to Get Morale Up in Down Times	ILC Tape	$12.00	C5094

16. The Law of the _____

Momentum is a Leader's Best Friend

Many times, the only difference between winning and losing is _____.

Momentum is the _____ !

Momentum makes leaders _____ better than they are.

Momentum makes followers _____ better than they are.

No momentum makes leaders look _____than they are.

No momentum makes followers _____ worse than they are.

Leaders are like _____ — They control the temperature.

Followers are like _____ — They record the temperature.

How to Move the Big Mo

(1) Understand it's _____.

(2) _____what the motivating factors are in your organization.

(3) _____the de-motivating factors in your organization.

(4) Schedule times for _____ and _____.

(5) _____ and _____ people who move the ball forward.

(6) Practice _____ Leadership.

Questions:

(1) What are the motivating factors of my organization? _____

_____

(2) What are the de-motivating factors of my organization? _____

_____

(3) What am I doing to increase the motivating factors? _____

_____

(4) What am I doing to decrease the de-motivating factors? _____

_____

Evaluate Your Mastery of the Law of the Big Mo. (1–10) _____

Resources: Momentum, the Best Friend a Leader Ever Had   ILC Tape $12.00   C5086
How to Regain Lost Momentum   ILC Tape $12.00   C5131

To order these resources or for more information please call 1-800-333-6506

17.The Law of _____

Leaders Understand that Activity is Not Necessarily Accomplishment

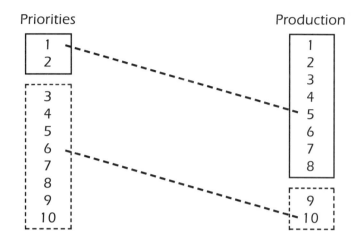

Priorities   Production

The 3 Priority Questions:

R _____ What is required of me?

R _____ What gives me the greatest return?

R _____ What gives me the greatest reward?

JM's 4 Priorities: (1) _____ (3) _____

(2) _____ (4) _____

Questions:

(1) What are my top 20% priorities? _____

(2) Who are my top 20% people? _____

_____

Evaluate Your Mastery of the Law of Priorities. (1–10) _____

Resources: Priorities — The Pathway to Success   Video Kit $119.95   V3010
Developing the Leader Within You   Book $17.95   B2014

18. The Law of _____

A Leader Must Give Up to Go Up

"For everything you gain, you must lose something." —Emerson

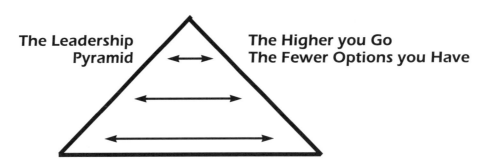

The Leadership Pyramid

The Higher you Go
The Fewer Options you Have

Sacrifice Statements:

(1) There is no success without _____ .

(2) The _____ the level of leadership — the greater the sacrifice.

(3) You have to give up to _____ .

What got you there won't keep you there.
The greatest threat to tomorrow's success is _____ success.

Questions:

(1) What is my next level of growth that I must climb and conquer? _____

(2) What will I have to give up? _____

(3) Am I willing to do it? _____

_____

_____

Evaluate Your Mastery of the Law of Sacrifice. (1–10) _____

Resource:	Ten Tradeoffs Usually Worth Making	ILC Tape	$12.00	C5118
	How to Fail Forward	ILC Tape	$12.00	C5116

19. The Law of _____

When to Lead is as Important as What to Do and Where to Go

"Make hay while the sun shines — that's smart;
go fishing during the harvest — that's stupid." —Prov. 10:7 (The Message)

The Wrong Action at the Wrong Time = _____

The Wrong Action at the Right Time = _____

The Right Action at the Wrong Time = _____

The Right Action at the Right Time = _____

The Law of Timing is a Double-Edged Sword!

Timing Requires . . .

(1)_____ (4)_____

(2)_____ (5)_____

(3)_____ (6)_____

(7)_____

Note: The Laws of Intuition and Timing are the two most difficult to teach.

Questions:

(1) Review the requirements of Timing. What are your weak areas? _____

_____

(2) Who should you ask to help you in this area? _____

Hint: Naturally-gifted Leaders excel in this area.

Evaluate Your Mastery of the Law of Timing. (1–10) _____

Resources:	When to Move in Leadership	ILC Tape	$12.00	C5056
	Insights About Intuition	ILC Tape	$12.00	C507A
	Decision Making	Audio Kit	$45.00	T1121

20.The Law of _____

To Add Growth, Lead Followers — To Multiply, Lead Leaders

Followers Math = _____

Leaders Math = _____

_____ % of all leaders, gather followers, not leaders!

Why? (1)Leaders are hard to _____.

(2)Leaders are hard to _____.

(3)Leaders are hard to _____.

The Differences Between { Leaders who Develop Leaders & Leaders who Develop Followers }

(1) _____

Leaders who develop Followers . . . _____

Leaders who develop Leaders . . . _____

(2) _____

Leaders who develop Followers focus on the _____ of people.

Leaders who develop Leaders focus on the _____ of people.

(3) _____

Leaders who develop Followers devote attention to the _____ 20%.

Leaders who develop Leaders devote attention to the _____20%.

(4) _____

Leaders who develop Followers are _____ Leaders.

Leaders who develop Leaders are _____ Leaders.

(5) _____

Leaders who develop Followers lift up _____.

Leaders who develop Leaders lift up _____.

(6) _____

    Leaders who develop Followers _____ time with people.

    Leaders who develop Leaders _____ time with people.

(7) _____

    Leaders who develop Followers ask for _____ commitment.

    Leaders who develop Leaders ask for _____ commitment.

(8) _____

    Leaders who develop Followers lead everyone the _____.

    Leaders who develop Leaders lead everyone _____.

(9) _____

    Leaders who develop Followers impact _____ generation.

    Leaders who develop Leaders impact _____ generation.

My friend Dale Galloway says, *"Some leaders want to make followers. I want to make leaders. Not only do I want to make leaders, but leaders of leaders. And then, leaders of leaders of leaders."*

Questions:

(1) What is my leadership # ? _____

    Note: That will determine the quality of person you attract.

(2 Review the Nine Differences between Leaders who develop Leaders and Leaders who

    develop Followers. Which side do you fall on? _____

_____

_____

Evaluate Your Mastery of the Law of Explosive Growth. (1–10) _____

Resources: *Developing the Leaders Around You*   Book $17.95   B2057
           Developing the Leaders Around You   Video $199.00   B2057K

21. The Law of _____

A Leader's Lasting Value is Measured by Succession

"Succession is one of the key responsibilities of leadership."
—Max Depree, *Leadership is an Art*

_____ comes when someone is able to do great things _____

_____.

_____ comes when he empowers followers to do great things

_____.

_____ comes when he develops leaders to do great things

_____.

_____ comes when he raises his organization to do great things

_____.

Questions:

(1) When I leave a responsibility does it get better or worse? Why? _____

_____

(2) Have I handed the leadership baton off to the next leader with integrity and a solid foundation to continue the success of the organization? _____

_____

_____

Evaluate Your Mastery of the Law of Legacy. (1–10) _____

Resources:	Transitioning with Integrity	Video / Audio Kit	$99.95	V3013
	Success calls for a Successor	ILC Tape	$12.00	C5121

To order these resources or for more information please call 1-800-333-6506

Personal Review and Evaluation of the 21 Laws   1—10

1. The Law of the **Lid** — Leadership Determines the Level of Effectiveness

---

2. The Law of **Influence** — The True Measure of Leadership is Influence — Nothing More, Nothing Less

---

3. The Law of **Process** — Leadership Develops Daily, Not in a Day

---

4. The Law of **Navigation** — Anyone Can Steer the Ship, but it Takes a Leader to Chart the Course

---

5. The Law of **E.F. Hutton** — When the Real Leader Speaks, People Listen

---

6. The Law of **Solid Ground** — Trust is the Foundation of Leadership

---

7. The Law of **Respect** — People Naturally Follow Leaders Stronger than Themselves

---

8. The Law of **Intuition** — Leaders Evaluate Everything Through a Leadership Bias

---

9. The Law of **Magnetism** — Who you Are is Who You Attract

---

10. The Law of **Connection** — Leaders Touch a Heart Before they Ask for a Hand

---

11. The Law of the **Inner Circle** — A Leader's Potential is Determined by Those Closest to Him

---

12. The Law of **Empowerment** — Only Secure Leaders Give Power to Others

---

13. The Law of **Reproduction** — It Takes a Leader to Raise Up a Leader

---

14. The Law of **Buy—In** — People Buy Into the Leader, Then the Vision

---

15. The Law of **Victory** — Leaders Find a Way for the Team to Succeed

---

16. The Law of the **Big Mo** — Momentum is a Leader's Best Friend

---

17. The Law of **Priorities** — Leaders Understand that Activity is Not Necessarily Accomplishment

---

18. The Law of **Sacrifice** — A Leader Must Give Up to Go Up

---

19. The Law of **Timing** — When to Lead is as Important as What to Do and Where to Go

---

20. The Law of **Explosive Growth** — To Add Growth, Lead Followers to Multiply, Lead Leaders

---

21. The Law of **Legacy** —A Leader's Lasting Value is Measured by Succession

---

Date_____

Personal Review and Evaluation of the 21 Laws   1—10

1. The Law of the **Lid** — Leadership Determines the Level of Effectiveness

---

2. The Law of **Influence** — The True Measure of Leadership is Influence — Nothing More, Nothing Less

---

3. The Law of **Process** — Leadership Develops Daily, Not in a Day

---

4. The Law of **Navigation** — Anyone Can Steer the Ship, but it Takes a Leader to Chart the Course

---

5. The Law of **E.F. Hutton** — When the Real Leader Speaks, People Listen

---

6. The Law of **Solid Ground** — Trust is the Foundation of Leadership

---

7. The Law of **Respect** — People Naturally Follow Leaders Stronger than Themselves

---

8. The Law of **Intuition** — Leaders Evaluate Everything Through a Leadership Bias

---

9. The Law of **Magnetism** — Who you Are is Who You Attract

---

10. The Law of **Connection** — Leaders Touch a Heart Before they Ask for a Hand

---

11. The Law of the **Inner Circle** — A Leader's Potential is Determined by Those Closest to Him

---

12. The Law of **Empowerment** — Only Secure Leaders Give Power to Others

---

13. The Law of **Reproduction** — It Takes a Leader to Raise Up a Leader

---

14. The Law of **Buy—In** — People Buy Into the Leader, Then the Vision

---

15. The Law of **Victory** — Leaders Find a Way for the Team to Succeed

---

16. The Law of the **Big Mo** — Momentum is a Leader's Best Friend

---

17. The Law of **Priorities** — Leaders Understand that Activity is Not Necessarily Accomplishment

---

18. The Law of **Sacrifice** — A Leader Must Give Up to Go Up

---

19. The Law of **Timing** — When to Lead is as Important as What to Do and Where to Go

---

20. The Law of **Explosive Growth** — To Add Growth, Lead Followers to Multiply, Lead Leaders

---

21. The Law of **Legacy** —A Leader's Lasting Value is Measured by Succession

---

Date_____